# THE GREAT CRESTED GREBE

## K. E. L. SIMMONS

## CONTENTS

Cover: *An adult Great Crested Grebe and its reflection.*

Series editor: Jim Flegg.

Copyright © 1989 by K. E. L. Simmons. First published 1989.
Number 37 in the Shire Natural History series. ISBN 0 7478 0019 7.

Printed in Great Britain by C. I. Thomas & Sons (Haverfordwest) Ltd, Press Buildings, Merlins Bridge, Haverfordwest, Dyfed.

# Introduction

With its striking appearance and fascinating habits, the Great Crested Grebe (*Podiceps cristatus*) has strong claims to be considered the most beautiful and interesting of all European waterfowl. Its basic plumage, worn briefly in autumn and early winter, is counter-shaded (dark above and pale below) with a blackish crown, from the rear of which projects a distinctive double crest. Viewed from in front, this large grebe looks almost wholly pale, the face, foreneck and that part of the upper breast showing above the waterline being conspicuously white.

But it is in nuptial or display plumage that it is at its loveliest: then the crown crest is darker and longer and the white face framed on each side with a dense ruff or 'tippet' of plush chestnut and black feathers. Like the crest, the tippets are erectile and play an important role in the bird's complex displays, in which both sexes take part.

Male and female are alike in both appearance and behaviour. Most females, however, are rather smaller than the males, with slightly shorter crests and smaller, sometimes less bright tippets. They usually have somewhat shorter and thinner bills too, such differences being most obvious when mates are seen together. The male is always the taller of the two when they are engaged frontally in full mutual courtship display.

Long of neck, with a dagger-shaped bill and streamlined body, the Great Crested Grebe is superbly designed for diving, swimming underwater and catching fish. As with all the other grebes, the tail is vestigial, a mere tuft of soft feathers. The powerful feet, with their lobed semi-webbed toes, are set at the rear of the body with only the laterally compressed tarsus and the very end of the tibia exposed. The joint between these is so flexible that the tarsus and toes, as well as being moved forward and backward (either alternately or together), can be rotated rather like a propellor, giving the bird great manoeuvrability underwater. Not used for swimming, the wings are relatively small with decurved primaries that fit closely against the contour of the body and lie hidden away for much of the time beneath the long flank feathers. In keeping with the grebe's almost wholly aquatic life, the satiny white plumage of the underparts, comprising some five thousand small feathers (of a total of fourteen thousand), is particularly dense.

The Great Crested is the largest of the five European grebes, two of which – the Slavonian or Horned Grebe (*Podiceps auritus*) and the Red-necked Grebe (*P. grisegena*) – are probably its nearest relatives in a family of some 23 species. The Black-necked or Eared Grebe (*P. nigricollis*), though a member of the same genus, is rather less closely related, its affinities lying with three other eared grebes (one of which is now extinct) and with the Hooded Grebe (*P. gallardoi*), all of which are found only in South America. The fifth European grebe, the Dabchick or Little Grebe (*Tachybaptus ruficollis*), is still more distantly related to all these.

## RANGE

The Great Crested Grebe has a wide distribution in the Old World but is found mainly in the temperate parts of Europe and Asia. It reaches southern Europe, North Africa, the Middle East and South Africa but, except in Spain, its numbers are quite small, as they are in tropical Africa where it is confined to the cooler altitudes of the highland lakes. Absent from most of the Indian subcontinent, and from southern Asia, Japan and the Australian islands, it reappears in parts of Australia and New Zealand. In North America, its place as a specialist fish-eater is taken by the Red-necked Grebe and by the Western Grebe (*Aechmophorus occidentalis*) and its sibling species Clark's Grebe (*Ae. clarkii*).

In the British Isles, the Great Crested Grebe is at the western fringe of its huge range. England is its stronghold here, especially the midland and southern counties, but it is absent as a breeder in most of the south-west. The species becomes less common the further west it extends into Wales and the further north into Scotland, being almost absent north and west of the central lowlands. Although not uncommon in Ireland, it is again largely confined to the lowland areas.

1. *A group of Great Crested Grebes in winter– adults and a juvenile.*

## HABITAT

Great Crested Grebes breed mainly on eutrophic, standing freshwater lakes, larger ponds and the like, both natural and artificial, with areas of fringing vegetation in which nests can be sited and a sufficient expanse of open water in which to fish, ideally at depths of 3 to 4 metres. The birds are also found occasionally on slow-flowing rivers and brackish estuaries. When breeding is over, some birds remain to moult on the same waters; they may depart afterwards or stay and winter there, leaving only if the site ices over. Many others, however, disperse after breeding to undergo their moult elsewhere, resorting, sometimes in considerable numbers, to certain traditional waters: large lakes, estuaries, or the sea close inshore. These provide protection as well as food, for after breeding the adult grebe sheds all its wing feathers simultaneously and becomes flightless for a period of three to four weeks. Most birds then remain at the moult refuge until returning to the breeding waters, though some make proper migrations south to warmer climes.

The five European grebes are mainly separated by their differing ranges or choice of habitat and diet. Where the fish-eating Great Crested occurs on the same water as any of the others, it is the dominant species, the Red-necked Grebe (which alone of the five does not breed in the British Isles) being its main potential competitor. Within the area of overlap, however, the Red-necked, which elsewhere is a fish-eater, has had to change its diet in order to exist alongside its larger relative, with a corresponding reduction in the size of its bill. This is a good example of what is now termed 'character displacement'.

## THE GREBE AND MAN

When white 'grebe-fur' (the thick underpelt) was favoured in women's fashion during the second half of the eighteenth century, especially to make shoulder capes and mufflers (or 'tippets' in the original meaning of the word), the Great Crested Grebe was killed commercially on a large scale to satisfy the demands of the millinery trade, which quickly brought it to the edge of extinction.

By 1860 there were fewer than forty pairs left in England and it took the combined efforts of a pioneering series of Bird Protection Acts (the last in 1880) to save it. Since then, and particularly during the twentieth century, the species has flourished and its numbers within the British Isles have risen considerably, with a corresponding increase of range, especially into Scotland. This improvement in the grebe's fortunes was aided, in the first place, by a more enlightened public attitude to bird conservation and, later, by the accidental provision of many new waters suitable for breeding, chiefly flooded gravel-pits, which are often stocked with fish by angling societies.

Though it is rare now for grebes to be shot by 'sportsmen' or persecuted by anglers for daring to eat fish at all (and, one suspects, for often appearing to be more successful in catching them than the man on the bank), they are now faced by new dangers from the modern world. These include the deleterious effects of organochlorine pesticides and other agricultural chemicals, the impact of which remains to be fully assessed, and the disturbance caused on many large lakes, reservoirs and gravel-pits by the activities of the late twentieth-century leisure industry (water-skiing, power-boating, yachting and fishing in particular but also rambling and even birding in some cases).

## GREBE WATCHING

Large and conspicuous, Great Crested Grebes are easy birds to watch, especially where they become used to seeing people and are not harassed by them. Away from the nest (where they should never be disturbed), they spend much of their time in full view on open water doing many noteworthy things.

Their courtship is conducted mostly out on the water for all to see, as are the rituals of hostility connected with defence of the mate, territory and brood. Much of the parental care of the young, an aspect of the life history that has been neglected by most students of grebe biology, can also be observed from a vantage point on the bank. The chicks themselves are an endless source of interest and entertainment. Then there are the everyday habits to watch: the routine of alternately fishing and loafing, and the feeding and comfort behaviour that goes with it.

To those who find all such topics of little interest, there remains census work of one type or another, for the Great Crested Grebe is an easy bird to count, especially outside the breeding season. There is a vast body of past information already available to check against, assembled by both the British Trust for Ornithology and the Wildfowl Trust. In the breeding season, however, one must account for incubating birds and be aware that broods may be divided (see below).

# The grebe's day

At its simplest, the daily routine of a Great Crested Grebe consists of repeated alternations of clear-cut spells of fishing and bouts of loafing during which it attends to its toilet and rests. These activities of self-maintenance are vital to its survival.

## FOOD AND FEEDING

The Great Crested Grebe is primarily piscivorous, specialising in catching a wide range of freshwater species, although it will take a variety of other, mainly invertebrate prey such as aquatic insects. Most often it catches deep-bodied coarse fish, including roach, perch, dace, chub, rudd, tench, bleak and bream. These are of most age-classes, including fry, up to a maximum width of about 7.5 cm and a maximum length of about 22 cm, or longer in the case of thin-bodied species such as eels. It will also take game species such as trout but fish of this type form a quite unimportant proportion of its diet.

Most food is caught under water by *dive-hunting*. On the surface, the grebe first sinks low in the water and reduces its buoyancy by sleeking the plumage; it then submerges by diving head-first, usually in a seemingly effortless manner with a quick forward and downward swing of the neck and a powerful push of its feet. Below the surface, it swims about looking for prey, which is pursued rapidly if sighted. Though it operates like this mainly in deeper water free of plants, it will also thread its way through patches of vegetation, provided these are not too dense, picking up what it can find as it passes.

All prey is seized between the tips of the mandibles, most smaller items being eaten under water but large ones retained and dealt with after the bird resurfaces; this also happens with smaller prey caught at the end of a dive or those that cause problems (as sticklebacks do with their sharp

2 (Top left). *The Slavonian Grebe: a bird at the nest. Note the red eye and golden 'horn' on the side of the head. Unlike the Great Crested and Little Grebes, this species and the Red-necked and Black-necked Grebes occur in North America as well as in Europe.*

3 (Top right). *The Red-necked Grebe. Note the grey and white face and the black crown and crest.*

4 (Bottom left). *The Black-necked Grebe: a bird carrying young on its back. Note the red eye, and the golden fan or 'ear' on the side of the head.*

5 (Bottom right). *The Little Grebe: a bird at the nest. Unlike the other European grebes, this species lacks elongated head feathers in any plumage.*

6. *A Great Crested Grebe in flight. Note the wing pattern and the characteristic shape of a flying bird with feet extended behind.*

spines). Everything is swallowed whole as quickly as possible, fish head-first and side-on, often while still alive. Larger and difficult specimens take longer.

Sometimes a grebe will catch a fish that is too big and then abandon it. This is especially true of female grebes, which, though capable of catching fish of the maximum size that the males can eat, cannot manage to swallow them.

Unless it catches its fill on the first dive, the grebe in each typical *hunting spell* makes one or more series of submergences, each such dive (which usually lasts between 16 and 25 seconds) being followed by a standard *pause* (of about 10 seconds) on the surface before the next dive. Each series of dives is separated by a somewhat longer *lull* before the next series starts.

The Great Crested Grebe will also search for prey without diving, largely by *surface-hunting* in shallow water or over beds of submerged water-plants. From a stationary position, or while swimming slowly along, it will peer below water with only its bill and face submerged, to just above eye level, often with a continuous and characteristic forward and backward 'shovelling' action, rather like a dog covering over a bone. It sometimes also scans from side to side. If prey is sighted the bird will dip its head and neck under the water to reach it or, with paddling feet, will up-end like a clumsy duck or even briefly 'submerse' its body, bobbing up again tail-first at the same spot. When diving or travelling under water from one spot to another, it surfaces head-first a good distance from the point of submersion.

Females tend to spend more time surface-hunting than males. Both sexes will also casually seize insects that are floating or swimming on the surface, or glean them from plants growing out of or over the water, or snatch flying insects from the air nearby, but only a negligible amount of their food is obtained in this way.

LOAFING

When the feeding spell is over, the grebe then takes a *loafing break*, usually swimming to a favourite resting spot on the water, especially one giving some shelter from wind or rain during inclement weather. Such breaks, like hunting spells, last from a few to many minutes, about 50 per cent of the available time being given to each. The duration of the loafing break, as of the feeding spell, and the total time spent feeding and loafing, depend on many factors, however, not least hunting success and the competition for available time between loafing, feeding and other activities — especially during the period of courtship and the rearing of young.

While making for the loafing spot the grebe often bathes. This ablution can vary from a few dips to a thorough wetting, with much splashing and diving; if the bird dives, the ensuing oiling and preening ses-

6

sion may be prolonged, special attention then being given to the wings.

During its break, the bird often also rests for a while (in the characteristic 'pork-pie' posture with the bill tucked into the side of the neck). At the end of the day it roosts at its last loafing spot for the night, but on moonlight nights the usual daytime activities may continue after dark.

## FEATHER CARE AND FEATHER EATING

Great Crested Grebes spend much of their time preening their feathers, mainly during loafing breaks, typically after bathing and oiling, but also at odd moments during diving pauses and lulls. The sight of a bird rolling over on its side to preen its underparts, exposing the white plumage of the opposite flank and belly as it nibbles away at individual feathers or quickly 'strops' whole areas of them with its bill, is a familiar and pleasing one.

While preening, a Great Crested Grebe will detach a feather from time to time, especially one of the small white ones from the breast and belly which are in a steady state of moult for much of the year. Though the feather may then be discarded, as the larger ones from the back or wing coverts usually are, the bird often deliberately eats it. Parent grebes will moreover give such feathers to the chicks from the day of hatching, even before they receive their first real feed. This strange habit is known only in members of the grebe family among all birds. There has been a great deal of discussion and controversy about the function of such feather eating. What are the facts?

First: most of the ingested feathers (largely from the breast and belly but also from the flanks and less frequently from other parts of the plumage) accumulate in the main chamber of the stomach where they break down into a greenish felt-like spongy material. This mixes with ingested food (mainly fish) and forms a characteristic *feather-ball*, which can fill the stomach.

Second: in addition to the feather-ball, a small mass of more or less whole ingested feathers forms a *feather-pad* in the lower chamber of the stomach, blocking the entrance to the intestine.

Third: unlike the feather-pad, the feather-ball, whole or in bits, is periodically regur-

gitated from the stomach together with its contents. These include the undigestible and more slowly digested parts of the food: scales, vertebrae and certain other harder bones, otoliths and the like from fish, and chitin from insects.

It would seem, then, that feathers are eaten for two main purposes. Firstly, the feather-ball forms the basis of ejectable pellets whereby the stomach can be cleared of surplus food remains, hence making room for fresh food. Secondly, the feather-pad forms a 'pyloric plug' in the lower stomach which prevents any non-food debris, including feather remains, from entering the intestine. The existence of known pellets from the Great Crested Grebe and the fact that no debris is to be found in its intestine support these two probabilities.

Further, work by Dutch ornithologists suggests that other, more potentially harmful items may be ejected from the stomach and prevented from entering the intestine by the grebe's unique secondary use of its own feathers. These include the endoparasites ingested along with the fish eaten. In support of this, it has been found that grebe gullets and stomachs are often remarkably free of heavy infestations of these in comparison with many other fish-eating birds. This protection is not absolute, however, for the grebes do harbour a variety of internal parasites including intestinal helminths (such as tapeworms and roundworms). Tapeworms in particular have a very complicated life-cycle, coming to the grebe via an intermediate host, often a fish, some individual birds becoming heavily infested.

## HELMINTH EATING

Stranger even than feather eating is the habit of some Great Crested Grebes of eating their own tapeworms and feeding them to the young, the worms being pulled from the cloaca with the bill or picked out of the water after they have been voided. A potentially rich source of nutrients (protein, fat and glycogen), especially when they contain eggs, they are relished by the grebe and evidently digested, the bird being able to take the risk of thus recycling its own parasites, or passing them on to its offspring, because its other habit of feather eating considerably reduces the danger of

7. *The strange Hooded Grebe of Patagonia: a loafing pair. This species was unknown to science until 1974.*

8. *The Western Grebe of North America: a bird carrying young.*

9. *A Great Crested Grebe about to dive below the water. The process of sleeking its feathers first is not quite completed.*

10. *A Great Crested Grebe swimming under water.*

re-infestation. Thus, perhaps because it was already a feather eater, the grebe could become a helminth eater too.

# The grebe's year

In some parts of its range, the Great Crested Grebe is able to nest almost throughout the year, pausing only to moult its wings. In the British Isles, however, it has to cope within the restrictions posed by a strict climatic regime, with a winter period which can bring low temperatures and ice. Consequently its breeding season in Britain is curtailed and of variable duration, depending on the severity of the weather.

## WINTER
During the four winter months November to February, those Great Crested Grebes which spend that season in Britain are engaged in a struggle for survival against the elements and may need to devote proportionately more of their time to obtaining sufficient food. They tend to associate in loose flocks when loafing between fishing spells, though each bird usually hunts on its own. Feeding flocks sometimes form over dense shoals of fish.

During the first part of the winter period, with the annual replacement of the wing feathers over, the grebes complete the full body moult that began in late summer. This is followed quickly by a partial moult, during which new tippets appear. The renewal of the white under-plumage, however, is slowed during the depth of the winter (when the birds are most in need of its thick protection) but continues at a steady rate for much of the rest of the year.

## PAIRING UP
Although the grebes need to give priority to their individual survival in winter, they also start to form pairs then – in early December in some cases – most mates having separated during or after the rearing of the last young of the previous season. Depending on the weather and the time available from fishing and other forms of

self-care, an increasing amount of water courtship occurs during January and February, even in birds whose head ornamentation is still poorly developed, and this continues into the spring.

Such display may start on the wintering waters and continue elsewhere later, the return to the breeding waters beginning in February. Those birds which have wintered there, sometimes still in their original pairs, or returned early may even proceed further with their reproductive cycle and establish themselves (in some cases even by the end of December) at potential nesting places, where they are ready to breed as soon as conditions are suitable.

## BREEDING SEASON
The key to the start of egg laying is the availability of places in which to site the nest as safely as possible from the attentions of predators, including man, by concealing it (usually in fringing vegetation) or by making it inaccessible (on islands, for example). This event is also influenced (accelerated or delayed) by other factors, in particular the weather, the water level and the food supply – which has to be sufficient for the female grebe to form her eggs and for male and female each to find the time to incubate them in turn.

These factors vary from water to water and from year to year. Thus, although the main laying season of the Great Crested Grebe in the British Isles extends from March to August, a very few first clutches may appear in February (exceptionally even by late January), especially in mild winters. Thus the birds may in some years be raising young from February or March to November or even December, though in most years from April to October.

## BREEDING STRATEGY
The Great Crested Grebe, like most other grebes, has to be an opportunistic breeder. By starting to nest as early in the year as it can rather than waiting until later, it stands the best chance of rearing the most young. In particular, it has more time to attempt two broods and to replace lost clutches and broods successfully. It cannot for certain, however, always time its breeding to coincide with conditions that are favourable for the raising of young, especially a plen-

tiful supply of small fish.

In consequence, it has evolved a complicated breeding strategy, the rules of which run something like this: (1) pair up and be ready to breed early; (2) take a chance at breeding as soon as a reasonably good site is available; (3) within the limits of the normal clutch size lay as many or as few eggs as feeding conditions at the time permit; (4) start incubating with the first egg laid so that the chicks hatch at intervals, thus giving the advantage to the older ones; (5) desert the last egg or two if conditions for the raising of young prove unfavourable at the time of hatching; (6) when the young are swimming freely, divide the brood and, particularly if feeding is difficult, favour only one chick in each family subgroup; (7) replace lost clutches and broods quickly; (8) attempt another brood if at all possible.

## SITES AND TERRITORIES

As soon as they can after pairing up, male and female together seek sites and establish or re-establish a territory, often well before suitable vegetation has appeared. Here, in the water off potential sites, they continue with their water courtship, which can be particularly intense and prolonged if close neighbours or intruders are present. Here sooner or later they will build platforms, mate and eventually nest.

Depending on such factors as local features of the habitat and population pressure, territories vary greatly in size. At one extreme they may be so small that the birds can use them only for nesting, at the other large enough for the birds to obtain all their food and raise their young. On some waters, where sites are few, the birds may form loose colonies, especially if there is a large reed-bed available to offer shelter and safety.

## SPRING

By the beginning of spring in March, many grebes are paired up and settled in their nesting territories; some have started to incubate, while a minority may even already be feeding young in certain years. A substantial number, however, will still be in the process of forming pairs and establishing themselves, with much display. So the great variety of activity and interest in the months of March and April makes

spring a particularly good time to watch grebes.

## SUMMER

Nesting continues throughout the period May to August, but water courtship has by this time virtually ceased, so the summer months are the best for studies of family life, and these may be continued into the autumn and early winter. When parental duties ease or cease, the adults shed their flight feathers (on the breeding water or elsewhere), the first birds in August (males often in advance of females). They also start their body moult, beginning to lose their tippets. The association between the mates may end then but some pairs remain together for the moult or beyond.

Though most Great Crested Grebes are dispersed as territorial breeding pairs in summer, those that have failed in their attempts to raise any young that season, or have been prevented from nesting, for example by the lack of suitable sites, tend to gather in loose flocks when loafing. There they may be joined later by the others for the moult, which continues in the autumn.

## AUTUMN

The autumn is a season of flux, as the majority of the birds change from their summer to their winter routine in September and October. It is a period of movement and moult, of the final breaking of ties with mate and young, and of the establishment of new regimes as the annual cycle completes its round.

# Courtship and mating

Famous among ornithologists and students of animal behaviour for their variety and complexity, the mutual displays of the Great Crested Grebe are performed during the process of pairing up and continue during the variable period of 'engagement' while the birds prepare, or wait, to nest. There are two main types: those that occur away from the site (water courtship) and those that occur at it (platform courtship).

11. *A Great Crested Grebe eating a large fish.*

12. *A parent Great Crested Grebe at the nest giving a feather to a recently hatched chick on its back.*

13. *The Cat-display of the Great Crested Grebe. As well as occurring in the Discovery and Retreat Ceremonies of courtship, this posture is used at times as a gesture of appeasement during hostilities.*

14. *A pair of Great Crested Grebes Head-shaking together.*

15. *Some everyday activities of the Great Crested Grebe. (From top left) Intense surface bathing; full resting posture (the 'pork pie'); the wing glide (a briefly held posture adopted from time to time during and after the oiling of the wings); oiling the back with the head; preening dorsally; and the preening roll.*

## WATER COURTSHIP

Though these displays have been well studied and had much written about them, they are even today often badly and inaccurately described in most popular texts. They comprise four distinctive rituals: the Head-shaking, the Discovery, the Retreat and the Weed Ceremonies. These occur, on their own or in combination with each other, when the two birds are stimulated to display together through the social activities of other grebes and, especially, when they meet after separation.

Such meetings often follow Advertising by one or both birds. Performed by grebes seeking a partner, or later by those that have lost sight of their mate or young, this is a mainly vocal display typical of the solitary bird. It gives a special croaking call with the neck stretched up, stopping as soon as visual contact is made.

The Head-shaking Ceremony is the most frequently enacted of all the grebe's courtship rituals, on its own and as the basis of the other three: as an introduction, a link or a sequel. In its simplest form, the two birds face with upstretched necks and both silently Head-shake, waggling their heads quickly upwards or swaying them slowly from side to side. This may be preceded by a more excited stage as the birds approach one another with lowered bills and rapidly waggling heads, uttering a characteristic ticking call. Head-shaking may merge into a third stage, Habit-preening, in which they repeatedly go through a formal mock preening movement, dipping down and back to lift one of the long scapular feathers on the back.

Sometimes, especially after total separation, the two grebes perform an even stranger ritual sequence: the Discovery Ceremony. One bird may first search for the other until, when they come closer, either of them then takes on the active role in the sequence by diving and approaching the partner underwater. It swims just below the surface so that its progress is indicated by a ripple. Meanwhile the second bird waits and, adopting a special hunched posture with the wings spread like a shield on each side of the body (the Cat-display), watches for the other to surface. It does so close by, suddenly rising in a weird vertical posture (the Ghostly-penguin Display), and the two birds then Head-shake together.

Head-shaking, especially after a Discovery, may lead to a third ritual: the Retreat

16. *Some further everyday activities of the Great Crested Grebe. (From top left)* Wing flap *('rise and flap'); full stretch; body shake ('rise and shake'); throat touch (to drain water from the bill); toes stretch (the foot is also shaken from this posture); and yawn.*

Ceremony. While the two birds are still Head-shaking, one of them suddenly patters off across the water, subsides well away from its partner and then turns to face it in another version of the Cat-display. The static bird meanwhile often seems to be taken by surprise; it may do nothing, or threaten, or itself go into the Cat-display. The two grebes may reunite and Head-shake together again, one sometimes then repeating the procedure.

Finally, Head-shaking may lead to the most spectacular of all the grebe's rituals: the Weed Ceremony. As the birds Habit-preen, they slowly turn and swim away from each other in a most formal manner, giving a twanging contact call, until, when well apart, first one and then the other dives in a slow, deliberate manner to seek weed. After a submergence of several seconds, the two reappear one after the other. They may find nothing or make do with, say, a twig; but if they are successful they both surface holding the desired large cargo of dank waterweed. They then close quickly and, when near, perform the Weed-dance together: suddenly rising up vertically breast to breast, treading water vigorously to maintain position, they swing their heads rapidly from side to side. After a few or many swings they subside and, discarding the weed, Head-shake again.

The sexes share the roles in three of these ceremonies equally but females initiate more Retreats than males. The displays appear to have had their main origins, long ago in the history of the species, in hostile encounters. They could perhaps be interpreted as a ritualised 'contest' by which male and female identify one another by sight and by their individually variable Advertising calls, test their suitability as potential mates, reduce the tensions between them, for grebes are non-contact, anti-social birds, and thus establish and maintain firm pair-bonds. The displays start out on open water before any sites are chosen (or available); then bouts just peter out. The Discovery, a ritual underwater attack and its appeasement, and the Retreat, a ritual escape and appeasement, are most characteristic of this early stage. The Weed Ceremony, however, which ends in a ritual fight, occurs at a later stage, when mating has started. Then, after a bout of water courtship, the pair will often retire to the site to continue with quite different activities there.

17. *Two rival Great Crested Grebes engaged in a vigorous fight.*

18. *Great Crested Grebes mating on their platform.*

19. *The Weed-dance. Both birds have failed to find weed here and have had to make do with twigs.*

## THREAT AND FIGHTING

Great Crested Grebes, even when flocking, are aggressive birds. So it is not surprising that, during and after pairing, the males especially get into disputes over mates, territory, nest sites and feeding spots. They will fight at times, fiercely grappling, stabbing and pecking as they clash and wrestle breast to breast with beating wings and much splashing, as if trying to drown one another; or one bird will attack another by pattering over the water at it or dive to spear it from under the water. Mostly, however, they depend more on a ritualised code of threat behaviour to expel or intimidate sexual or territorial rivals or intruders, using a variety of postures and actions backed up by calls, in particular a far-carrying barking one which serves as an all-purpose signal of self-assertion.

Threat consists mostly of a display in which the neck is extended and stretched forward with the bill close to the water, the bird at times ruffling up its back feathers or even 'swanning' up the wings. Another potent way of threatening is for a bird just to indicate that it might attack by pattering a

little way towards the rival over the surface or by diving and then coming up at almost the same spot.

## PLATFORM BEHAVIOUR

Great Crested Grebes can mate only out of water, usually on a specially built platform, though some pairs will make temporary use of a substitute site such as a small gravel islet or sloping bank. Like nests, mating platforms are typically constructed by male and female working together. They collect weed and other material, mainly from underwater by diving, and pile it up quickly on submerged plants, tree roots and the like, until the structure is just firm enough to support them; or they may build it up from the bottom in shallow water. Then one or other of the birds will ascend the platform and solicit by alternately Inviting (lying prone with extended neck), uttering intermittent twanging contact calls, and Rearing (rising suddenly with down-arched neck, quivering the wings in short bursts). The same Inviting behaviour is also sometimes performed, especially early in the season, on the water near potential mating sites, by one bird or by both simultaneously.

At first, matters at the platform do not proceed further than the pair building up the structure and taking turns to solicit upon it, but later either bird will also mount the other. Leaping up at the rear, it copulates then re-enters the water over the mate's head, all with characteristic calls. The two birds often Head-shake together afterwards, one in the water, one on the platform.

All this sexual activity may start weeks or months before any eggs are laid, so there is no question at first of true, functional mating: it is but a further stage of courtship — platform courtship. Only later, when the time of nesting comes, do the mountings by the male of the female lead to insemination and ovulation in the normal manner. Then egg laying and the raising of a family can proceed.

# Nesting and family life

With the onset of true mating, nest building continues in earnest, for a proper structure to hold the eggs is now needed; both sexes again participate. The true nest may be raised upon the old mating platform or be newly built elsewhere, for while almost any old site will do for mating the nest itself needs to be placed with more care.

## NEST AND EGGS

The nest of the Great Crested Grebe, though often quite bulky, lies mostly below water so the shallow cup itself is moist and dank. The normal clutch consists of two to six (usually three to five) plain whitish, chalk-covered eggs laid at two-day intervals. Incubation typically starts on the day that the first egg appears or very soon after. Male and female take turns in sitting on the eggs and relieving each other, so that the eggs are never left unattended unless the birds are disturbed. If alarmed, the incubating grebe quickly covers the clutch with loose nest material before it departs, thus hiding the eggs from the eyes of any predator. The eggs themselves, at first very conspicuous, soon become stained a brownish colour, thus adding to the camouflage. Each egg takes some 28 days to develop. The young do not hatch simultaneously,

20. *A Great Crested Grebe on the nest, about to settle down on its eggs.*

18

21. *A newly hatched Great Crested Grebe on the nest, not yet dry. Note the egg-shell remains, which the adult will remove on its return.*

therefore, but at the same intervals at which the eggs were laid. Thus, if they all survive, the last chick in a brood of four would arrive six to seven days after the first.

## THE CHICK

Alert and lively soon after it dries out from the egg, the Great Crested Grebe chick is one of the most striking and beautiful of all young birds. Clothed in down, it is striped dark brown and buff on the upper body and pure white below, with black and white stripes on the neck and head, a pattern of spots and lines round the face, and a black crown cap with a particularly conspicuous white crown spot at the rear. The short bill is also pied, with a pale 'egg-tooth' at its tip at first after hatching. On each side of its face, between bill and eye, is a large oval of bare purplish skin: the face patches. Even stranger is the small raised flange of bare wrinkled skin, roughly triangular in shape, on the fore-crown: the crown patch or 'tonsure'. When vascularised, all three patches, together with other areas of skin around the bill, flush and change colour, often becoming vividly red; the tonsure also swells greatly in size.

## CARRYING AND GUARDING

The tiny hatchling grebe does not remain under the sitting adult but, as soon as it is able, climbs up on to its parent's back where it is brooded cosily under the canopy provided by the tented wings. Grebes are among the few groups of birds which carry their young in this way. Unless disturbed, the chicks remain at the nest until all the brood has hatched, the parents taking turns to incubate the remaining eggs and to bring food to the young, also giving them feathers. As soon as the last chick is aboard, the nest is abandoned and the family takes to the water, the two adults continuing to alternate between carrying the young and feeding them, mainly on small, but increasingly larger, fish.

Though precocious and able to swim and dive soon after birth, the baby Great Crested Grebe does not immediately start

22. *The head of a small chick with its tonsure inflated. The face patches are starting to vascularise also, as is the skin at the base of the bill.*

swimming about and finding its own food as a duckling does but is dependent on parental feeding for many weeks. At first it also relies on its parents for warmth, sheltering on their backs, for it is particularly vulnerable to chilling when small. The chick has an aversion for the water during the first twelve days or so of life, seldom leaving the parental back except if deliberately evicted by the adults. This mostly happens when the adults change over in their carrying duties, the chicks soon scrambling aboard again. For the first four or so days of life only, the young grebe, like a nestling passerine, produces its faecal droppings enclosed in a sac, depositing them on the parent's back.

The carrying stage lasts for nearly three weeks, though the older young, their down now fully waterproof, spend an increasing amount of time in the water before this, a position there close to the carrying parent giving them the first chance of intercepting food that the other adult brings. Even after carrying has ceased, the old birds may take turns in guarding the chicks for a further two weeks or so, but if food is scarce they may both have to work simultaneously before this is in order to find enough for the growing brood to eat.

## FAMILY ORGANISATION

Siblings establish themselves into a simple age hierarchy during the first weeks away from the nest, fighting at times and showing submission by hiding the bill. Later, when carrying is over, families of more than one surviving chick tend to be divided between the parents, this system becoming stable by the sixth week at the latest, each adult by then typically caring only or mainly for its 'own' young. Especially when enforced strictly, such *brood division* greatly improves the efficiency of each adult's feeding rate, the chicks in a subgroup receiving more food than when the family was undivided. Though the members of the two units often remain in loose contact, gathering when loafing, they may go their own ways. The adults usually show hostility to the 'other' young, sometimes even to one another. To complicate matters even fur-

20

ther, each parent also shows favouritism to a single chick within its own group. This 'in-chick' is given precedence in feeding over any others, the 'out-chicks', to which the adult may also be aggressive, especially if food is scarce.

Relationships between chicks and parents become increasingly tense, starting from the time when the adults refuse to carry them any more. The young grebes are highly vocal, keeping up a continual 'attention-demanding' piping call when pestering the loafing adults. Variants of this call are uttered when chicks approach them to take food, when they flee, or when they are lost or distressed. Out-chicks, especially, also perform a variety of appeasing, submissive and begging displays. These include demonstrations in which they call, splash up water with the feet, sink low with the tail-end elevated, gape widely, flush the bare patches on the head — and 'present' the face for identification — each chick having its own individual pattern of spots and lines, as well as vocal characteristics, by which the adults recognise it. The in-chick, especially, may perform a kind of Parent Discovery when joining 'its' adult, diving up to it and swimming about it under the water, periodically surfacing the head only like a periscope. When the members of a sub-brood are loafing together, the in-chick can be recognised as the one in close and intimate proximity to the parent, perhaps cadging feathers. Any out-chicks present will be the ones keeping their place silently on the periphery of the group, ready to flee and often adopting the pork-pie resting posture as a signal of appeasement, with the tonsure inflated and conspicuously red.

DEVELOPMENT OF THE YOUNG

The young grow fast and replace their down with feathers, except on the upper neck, head and face, where they retain their individually distinctive patterning throughout the period they are with the parents. They reach full body size in just over seven weeks and their wings are full-grown about a week later, though they cannot yet fly. The bare flushing areas on the face fill in with white feathers after six to seven weeks, while the tonsure shrivels and finally disap-

*23. A two-day old chick. Note the shrunken tonsure and compare with figure 22.*

21

24. *A family of Great Crested Grebes. The chick aboard the female is being given a feather by the male.*

pears between the growing crown feathers after about eight.

The young start diving and going through They may manage to catch the odd gnat but do not start to obtain fish of their own until about five weeks old and then mostly by luck. Not until their eighth or ninth week are they beginning to catch fish efficiently for themselves by diving. They then quickly become more adept and can be independent of their parents for food from the tenth week onwards. They remain with them, however, at least one week later, making their first flight in that week or the next. They may then depart but some stay on longer, in-chicks still receiving food from the parents up to the thirteenth week, occasionally longer.

INDEPENDENCE

After severing their family ties, the young grebes tend to flock with other juveniles at first. They often engage in brief bouts of water courtship together (mainly Head-shaking), as they did with their siblings from as early an age as three weeks. They may even climb out on the bank and solicit, but such behaviour is disorganised and spasmodic. Later the juveniles merge with the wintering adults. They first breed as adults when they are two years old.

FURTHER BROODS

If they can, the parents will attempt to raise a second brood, but only if they have nested early enough and the first family was small. The two broods are usually overlapped, the second clutch being laid when the earlier young are six to seven weeks old, but conditions are evidently seldom favourable for double brooding in Britain and most successful pairs raise just the one brood.

# The grebe watchers

The Great Crested Grebe is a bird with a notable history in the ornithology of the British Isles. Today we tend to take it rather for granted but to earlier generations of bird-watchers it was, as a species brought back from the very brink of extinction, almost an object of veneration and certainly a subject of special attention. Now one of the better studied British birds, its habits and life history were still largely unknown even after the turn of the twentieth century. During an age in which the gun rather than the glass was a naturalist's best friend, no one seems to have taken a serious look even at any of its spectacular displays.

Then came the pioneering observations on the bird's behaviour by Edmund Selous at Culford Lake in Suffolk in 1901 and 1902, and by J. S. Huxley at Tring in Hertfordshire in 1910. This work was followed up later by W. P. Pycraft, Henry Boase, David Gunn, L. S. V. Venables, Selous again (at Tring in 1915) and the bird photographers Miss E. M. Turner, Charles R. Brown, Oswald J. Wilkinson and Niall Rankin.

Julian Huxley's later observations near Oxford in the early 1920s, made with the help of his students and members of the local bird society, may have been the first of those co-operative studies that have become such a feature of modern bird study in Britain, especially after the formation of the British Trust for Ornithology in 1933. Already in 1931, however, there had been an ambitious national enquiry organised by T. H. Harrisson and P. A. D. Hollom into the status and habits of the Great Crested Grebe in England, Wales and Scotland. Later censuses and sample counts were continued by the BTO itself but have now, alas, been discontinued.

The author's own studies stretch back to 1948 and are still progressing. They grew from the simple desire of a young bird-watcher, keen to know all about the way that birds live and behave, to see for himself something of those spectacular courtship displays of the Great Crested Grebe that he had read about in books. He had no idea, then, that he was embarking upon an exciting journey of new discovery and understanding of the whole biology of his chosen species; indeed he was soon told by a famous ornithologist in Oxford that 'It's all been done, you know'. It had not all been done before, nor has it yet, so there is still scope for a young bird-watcher even today to add to our knowledge of this wonderfully fascinating waterbird.

*25. A family subgroup: parent and two chicks. The adult is alert, with neck erect and plumage sleeked.*

# Further reading

Boase, H. 'On the Display and Nesting of the Great Crested Grebe in Scotland', *British Birds*, volume 18, 1925.

Cramp, S., and Simmons, K. E. L. (editors). *The Birds of the Western Palearctic (Handbook of the Birds of Europe, the Middle East, and North Africa)*, volume 1. Oxford University Press, London, 1977.

Fjeldså, Jon. *Grebes*. AV-media, Copenhagen, 1977.

Gunn, D. 'The Fighting Methods of the Great Crested Grebe', *British Birds*, volume 22, 1928.

Harrisson, T. H., and Hollom, P .A. D. 'The Great Crested Grebe Enquiry, 1931' *British Birds*, volume 26, 1932.

Huxley, J. S. 'The Courtship Habits of the Great Crested Grebe', *The Proceedings of the Zoological Society of London*, 1914.

Huxley, J. S. 'Some Further Notes on the Courtship Behaviour of the Great Crested Grebe,' *British Birds*, volume 18, 1924.

Melde, M. *Der Haubentaucher*. A. Ziemsen Verlag, Wittenburg Lutherstadt, 1970.

Pycraft, W. P. 'Habits of the Great Crested Grebe', *The Field*, volume 118, 1911.

Selous, E. 'An Observational Diary of the Habits — Mostly Domestic — of the Great Crested Grebe', *The Zoologist*, 1901, 1902.

Selous, E. 'The Sex-habits of the Great Crested Grebe', *The Naturalist*, 1920-21.

Simmons, K. E. L. 'Studies on Great Crested Grebes', *The Avicultural Magazine*, volume 61, 1955.

Simmons, K. E. L. 'Grebe', in A. Landsborough Thompson (editor), *A New Dictionary of Birds*. Nelson, London, 1964.

Simmons, K. E. L. 'Adaptations in the Reproductive Biology of the Great Crested Grebe', *British Birds*, volume 67, 1974.

Simmons, K. E. L. 'Further Studies on Great Crested Grebes', 1-2, *Bristol Ornithology*, volumes 8 and 10, 1975 and 1977.

Simmons, K. E. L. 'Grebe', in Bruce Campbell and Elizabeth Lack (editors), *A Dictionary of Birds*. T. and A. D. Poyser, Calton, 1985.

Venables, L. S. V., and Lack, D. 'Territory in the Great Crested Grebe', *British Birds*, volume 28, 1934.

Venables, L. S. V., and Lack, D. 'Further Notes on Territory in the Great Crested Grebe', *British Birds*, volume 30, 1936.

Vlug, J. J. *De Fuut*. Koninklijke Nederlandse Natuurhistorische Vereninging, 1983.

ACKNOWLEDGEMENTS
I would like to thank Mr R. J. Prytherch for drawing the text figures and the following for their photographs: Mr W. N. Charles, 18, 20, 21, 24, 25; Mr Jan van der Kam, cover 11, 14; the late Mr Paul Kop, 22, 23; Mr Chris Knights, 2, 5, 9, 10, 12, 19; Mr John Larsen, 1, 3, 4, 6, 17; Dr Gary L. Nuechterlein, 7, 8; and Mr T. G. Tuinman, 13. I am also grateful to Dr John Fjeldså, Dr R. W. Storer, and Mr J. J. Vlug for their help and to Dr Theunis Piersma for some recent information on feather eating and related topics.